THE (
WATC
NEIGHBOURHOOD, SOMERSET

Eric Robinson

Guide Series Editor;
J. T. Greensmith

A GUIDE TO THE GEOLOGY OF WATCHET
AND ITS NEIGHBOURHOOD, SOMERSET

by Eric Robinson

In the itineraries of this guide there are some locations where the exposures are still capable of various explanations. Several need the benefit of thought, weighing up alternative hypotheses. Even after more than 40 years field experience I do not know the answer to many of the questions posed. However, I like to think that this dilemma is both healthy and encouraging. Geology is never a closed book.

Although the country around Watchet may bring to mind Liassic fossil territory and a Jurassic zonal stratigraphy akin to that of Lyme Regis in Dorset there are many other features of the geology of the area of considerable interest. In a way this is a relief because very often the local Lias fails to live up to expectations. This is no Lyme Regis where fossils generally abound. Nearby Kilve and St Audriessuccessions are fossiliferous and little disturbed in the attitude of the beds but, by comparison, the Lias of the Watchet shores are never rich in the expected shelly fauna and are fiendishly faulted. Both areas are well described by Andy King in *Fossil Ammonites from the Somerset Coast*, an illustrated guide published in 1997 by Taunton Museum and English Nature.

It is salutary to draw attention to aspects of the Lias and the local New Red Sandstone which depart from the usual characteristics as described in many textbooks. This is also true for the Palaeozoic Old Red Sandstone rocks comprising the Quantock Hills and Exmoor, which are poorly exposed. They remain an enigma, nothing like the O.R.S. seen in the Welsh Borderland. Nonetheless, they are the immediate basement rocks for the Watchet area and the source of the much of the detritus for the subsequent Mesozoic strata from the Permian onwards. They must be assumed to have acted as a basement control on subsequent Jurassic and Tertiary stresses which produced the faulted disarray of the shorelands.

Of growing geological interest are the mineral deposits of the Brendon Hills (northeast corner of Exmoor) currently the subject of a Heritage Lottery bid aimed to highlight the mining of haematite iron ore, the mines and the mineral railway system which served the mines between 1855 and 1917. Two itineraries included here follow part of the mineral line from Watchet. The Town Museum in Watchet on the edge of the harbour has all the appeal of an Aladdin's Cave. There is a splendid model of a typical Brendon Hill iron mine and the famous 1 in 4 incline on the Mineral Line. Moreover there is a full history of the Watchet ships and their trading, so important in the history of the coast. Local fossils, alabaster, books on the local landscape and ammonites are on view and admission is free.

Locally there is pride in the West Somerset Steam Railway which extends from Bishops Lydeard to Minehead. Brunel himself planned the extension of his 7ft

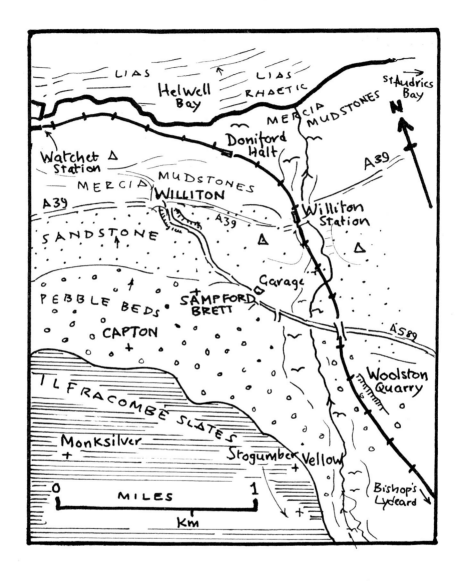

Figure 1. Sketch map of the geology of the Watchet area.

broad gauge track from Taunton when he recognised the commercial traffic which made the port of Watchet a prospering enterprise. Apart from the iron ore shipped to Ebbw Vale in South Wales from the West Quay, there was a brisk trade in Liassic limestone as a source of hydraulic lime, alabaster from the Triassic Mercia Marls to Bristol to make Plaster-of-Paris, as well as Devonian slates from the Brendon Hills prior to the competition from North Wales quarries. Welsh coal was brought to West Somerset and Devon by the branch line from 1860 supplementing that from the Bristol and Radstock Coalfields. Much of the history of the railway survives today along with the option of travelling by steam train but only from Bishops Lydeard as track connecting with the main line at Taunton is denied except for occasional 'specials'. There is an hourly connecting bus service from Taunton via Bishops Lydeard and Watchet to Minehead (Service 28, First Group).

In keeping with the times it is necessary to be safety conscious at all times.The cliffs, though not beetling and high, can nevertheless rain down shale flakes and harder pieces of limestone which can have hurtful impact. Some are landslip prone. Look before you approach, especially at Watchet West Beach and the Blue Anchor type section. At one time there were English Nature notice boards (now disappeared) asking that the cliffs should not be attacked, in other word no indicrimate hammering. This is good sense as most specimens are to be had by combing loose materials on the beach including exotic beach pebbles and boulders.

The Bristol Channel has a formidable tidal range and often the tides are wind-driven. It is tempting to follow outcrops offshore as the outer reefs are fossil-bearing Blue Lias. Try to study on a falling tide and take the advice of the local Coastguards if in any doubt. Note carefully the shale inlets which separate the harder limestone bands and quickly become flooded during rising tides and cut off escape routes.

The most useful map for getting around the area is the O.S. Landranger 1:50,000 No. 181 Minehead & Brendon Hills.

THE PALAEOZOIC FOUNDATIONS

The geology of the countryside around Watchet is largely post-Carboniferous, but it helps to look back to the Devonian and the subsequent Hercynian folding of the Palaeozoic succession to understand the facies and form of the Permo-Triassic and Jurassic rock developments as well as the events locally during the Pleistocene. The Devonian rocks of Exmoor and the Quantock Hills inlier are nothing like the familiar sequence of Old Red Sandstone sandstones, grits and conglomerates that can be seen in the Welsh Borderland. Rather they are grey sandstones of greywacke aspect and slaty measures, some of which in their graded bedded units resemble more closely the early Silurian Aberystwyth Grits. The Lower and Middle Devonian successions appear to have been deposited in subsiding basins with marginal deltaic, littoral and fluvial environments during a number of transgressive and regressive events. Occasional stabilisation allowed coral- and stromatoporoid-bearing limestone shelves to develop (Webby, 1965,1966).

Thicknesses are very difficult to determine but are considerable probably amounting to more than 5000 metres. Estimates are hampered by poor exposure and the folding and cleavage caused by Hercynian phases of compression. The best exposures can be seen along the lofty cliffs between Minehead and Porlock Bay, and then they really need to be viewed from a boat to gain a proper perspective. Minor folding builds up into the limbs of major folds on a scale best seen in the abandoned Triscombe Quarry, above the village of Crowcombe. (At present the quarry is 'out of bounds' as a Nature Reserve with nesting hawks, but may be accessible for distant viewing in the months to come). It is a measure of the poor exposure inland that this is the only sizeable outcrop worth citing.

The folded Devonian rocks make up two distinct massifs; Exmoor trending more or less west to east and the Quantocks inlier, east of Watchet and trending northwest to southeast. Both were subject to uplift and fault movements from time to time and contributed clastic debris into the adjacent low ground. The lowland between the massifs, essentially a half rift or half graben formed in pre-Jurassic times and even influencing Pleistocene deposition, is now marked by the valley from Taunton to the coast followed by road and rail to Watchet (Cope & Bassett, 1987).

As exposures inland are so poor it would take a long stay to piece together any meaningful understanding of either the succession or structure. However, there are small spot outcrops within a short bus journey from Watchet (Routes 28 and 38). At West Quantoxhead, in forestry plantations just above the large roadhouse on the corner of the A39 above the Victorian church of St Audries, there are old quarries which worked sandstones forming part of the Little Hangman Formation (Middle Devonian) (Edmonds, 1985). These were deposited in open marine, tidally influenced conditions. There is nearby parking and a picnic place (ST 114417).

Lower in the local sequence is the Trentishoe Grit Formation (lowest part of the Hangman Sandstone Group) which can be seen in narrow combes above the village of Bicknoller (ST 115399 and 121392) and further south in Halsway Combe (ST 135380). These combes are cut into the Quantock flanks and give easy access to slab stone, which was ideal for rubble masonry walling, rendered with lime sand mortar for dwellings, but also used directly in walling and sheepfolds. Some beds have a more slaty character and were used in roofing, although thatching was more common in the past (Webby, 1966). Overall the beds are interpreted as sheet-flood deposits probably of fluvial and lacustrine origin.

THE NEW RED SANDSTONE

Into the northwest-trending Doniford Valley, a half graben trough downfaulted in relationship to the Quantock Hills to the east and less so to the Brendon Hills to the west, clastics were flushed by vigorous sheet flooding as early as Permian times, although precise dates are difficult to confirm palaeontologically. Locally it has become convention to regard sandstones, breccias and marls lying below massive pebble beds and sandstones as 'Permian', the pebble beds being equated with the Budleigh Salterton Pebble Beds of south Devon and taken to be basal or Lower Triassic. This has its problems as will be outlined later, but it gives a basis for field mapping locally as far as Minehead and the coast.

Small outcrops of breccias and sandstones in contact with the Devonian, and faults of late Mesozoic age occur around the hamlet of Vexford, 1.6km south of Sampford Brett (ST 098387), but the massive pebble beds are seen most clearly in Woolston Quarry (ST 094403) (Figure 2). Close to the West Somerset Railway line the quarry was an important source of building stone for the bridges, culverts and station buildings throughout its 34km length. Currently it is owned by Mr. Hill of Sampford Brett, who gives permission to visit on prior request (tel. 01384-632825). Access is through fields at his milking parlour, so strict attention to gates, especially those giving access to the crossing of the line, is imperative. Parking needs to respect his access to the parlour from the narrow road running from the A358 to the hamlet of Woolston, a loop which returns to the A358.

Once in the quarry, stand back and look at the long quarry faces. The immediate impression will be of rapid lithological changes in the rocks when traced laterally and vertically. Sandstone lenses pinch out and channels cut down into lower beds. Closer inspection reveals graded bedding on a massive scale, with prominent pebble bases to the sandstones and channel infills. Sorting is poor, cobbles mixed up with pebbles and grains, giving clear evidence of sheet flood emplacement over short distances. The clast type is principally of quartzites, greywacke and vein quartz, materials not difficult to acquire from those nearby Quantocks combes cited above. There is another component in the mix, however, which requires some thought. It is a pale grey crystalline limestone containing thin shelled productid brachiopods and crinoid ossicles, both suggesting a Carboniferous age. But where was the source for this precise lithology? The pebble beds in the Budleigh Salterton area are said to have been laid down by a great river system draining northwards to the Midlands and perhaps the Bristol Channel area. *En route* there are Carboniferous outcrops, as in the Exe Valley at Bampton north of Tiverton, but they are exclusively in the slaty slab stone facies of the Culm of Devon and not in shelf limestone facies. Limestone lithologies do outcrop at Cannington, near Bridgwater, but they lie north of the Quantocks which must have existed as a barrier in Triassic times. The inference is that there might have been a northern source for the limestone pebbles at Woolston, possibly a Carboniferous shelf area linking the Mendips and South Wales (Martin, 1909). The channel fills need to be checked to see if the flow direction can be established. The issue is not decided.

While discussing the limestone clasts it is worth mentioning that many villages extending as far as Minehead had limekilns which used the clasts, supplemented by Lias beach boulders and Devonian limestone (the Roadwater Limestone within the Ilfracombe Slates south of Washford), for field lime and white renderings for farms and cottages.

The faces within Woolston Quarry are also notable for ruler-straight joints cutting through the varying lithologies which break them into bays and were features exploited by the quarrymen. At what point in time in the transition of wet,

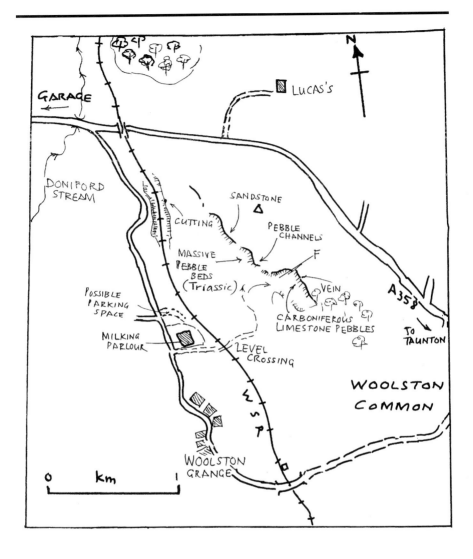

Figure 2. Sketch route map for Woolston Quarry.

weakly consolidated sediment could the stresses necessary to produce the joints, which pass clean through pebbles, have been generated? Furthermore, if the joint faces are examined some of them carry slickensides groovings which tell of inter-face movement, sometimes horizontally at other times vertically, as in faulting. In the southern part of the quarry substantial calcite veining follows the jointing. What post-Jurassic events account for all these structures?

Above the pebble beds, which regionally may reach about 40m in thickness, are sandstones as much as 250m thick regionally and commonly strongly cross-bedded in lenticular units. They are well seen in the lanes leading out of Sampford Brett, but most clearly by the A358 roadside leading uphill out of Williton towards Taunton (ST 081406 to 083406). These are best examined on foot as the road is busy with traffic and there is nowhere to park. The better sorted and more strongly cemented horizons were briefly quarried on the west side of the road. In the 19th century twelve to fifteen quarries were listed on the register for Williton, none of which survive, but the stone is well seen in the Methodist Church on the A358, the Police Station on the A39 road at Minehead and in the converted Workhouse on the A39 Bridgwater road. Toughest of the sandstones must be the deep red variety at Capton, a small hamlet west of Sampford Brett, which is still worked to meet the demand for 'local stone' asked for by Planners seeking to maintain local distinctiveness for West Somerset. Further exposures of the sandstones occur on roadside cliffs at Torre and near Hungerford, south of Washford, on the road to Roadwater (ST 046401/403).

In South Devon the sandstones above the Bunter Pebble Beds are referred to as the Otter Sandstones. However, it is necessary to be aware that correlation of the Watchet sandstones with South Devon can never be precise and Lower Sandstone could be a more convenient neutral term for use in the Bristol Channel coastal areas.

Geomorphologically, the outcrop of the Lower Sandstone in the Watchet area has been moulded into rounded-if-not-conical hills, about 60-70m high, and dissected by narrow valleys flowing off the Exmoor-Brendon Hills mass. The last phase of this dissection probably closely relates to periglacial activity during the warmer meltwater periods of the Pleistocene. This hilly fringe can be distinguished easily from the low coastal plain created on the outcrop of the late Triassic Mercia Mudstones, the latter being marked by strong red soils, as at Carhampton, Washford, Williton and Doniford.

When it comes to setting an upper limit to the Triassic succession it is tempting to regard the ending of the red marl lithology of the Mercia Mudstones, as seen at Blue Anchor (ST 035437) and West Beach, Watchet (ST 060437), as definitive especially when succeeded by other lithologies with drabber colour tones. Experience, however, tells us that the clearer and more obvious that boundary may be the more reason to suspect it as meaningful. What is missing when changes are abrupt ? And so it proves in Somerset sections where there are tempting colour contrasts at the top of the Triassic and at the base of the Jurassic. If the boundary is approached from above and the Liassic successions examined they are seen to comprise fluviatile sands, silts and local bone-beds interspersed with marine muds. In other words, transition is the true nature of the change as sections along the coast make clear.

The fullest and most complete unbroken sequences of the Mercia Mudstones are to be found in St Audrie's Bay (ST 105430), 5km east of Watchet, but in this guide the focus will be on the cliffs and foreshore at Blue Anchor almost 5km west

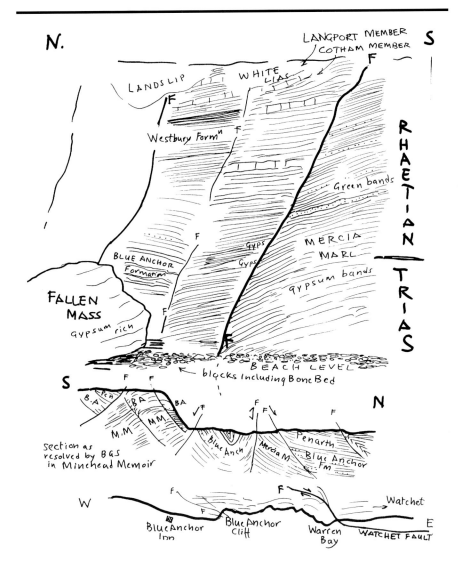

Figure 3. Structure and stratigraphy of the Blue Anchor cliffs.

of Watchet.

Blue Anchor is reached by the tortuous B3191 road which follows the cliff top and is served by an infrequent bus service (Blue Coaches twice or thrice a day). More excitingly, between March and October, a steam train can be taken on the West Somerset Railway from Watchet (a roughly hourly service on a single line).

The sea front at Blue Anchor is secured by a 900m seawall fronted by an 'armour' of massive limestone blocks. This protects reclaimed marshlands, once a large inlet of the sea extending as far as the walls of Dunster Castle (ST 992434). Access to the beach is gained by a cobbled slipway below the Blue Anchor Hotel, parking space existing on the landward side of the seafront. It is preferable to make a visit on a falling tide as it involves a walk along the sand at the edge of the boulder beach. The cliff offers clear evidence of the instability of the marls, with hollow 'scoop-outs' marking old landslips. This continues for about 700m to a point where foreshore rock ledges converge and begin to pass into the foot of a cliff of drab colours, banded and strung through with veins and seams of white gypsum. The red marls and drab bands come into near contact in a fault line with visible close-spaced jointing and drag in the marls (Fig. 3). This is a good point at which to take in the geometry of a normal fault exposed in the cliff face and extending across the horizontal surface of the foreshore. Similar faults will be seen on Watchet West Beach.

Grey and green siltstones and shales make up 3-4m of the drab bands, with occasional pebbles and nodules of gypsum hinting at changing environmental conditions from that of the Mercia Mudstone-type red marls. The input of silts indicates higher flow energies whereas mudcracks and gypsum as nodules and seams indicate phases of drying out. There are three distinct horizons of gypsum nodules, mostly about pebble size, and they represent a local correlatable stratigraphy between Blue Anchor and St Audrie's Bay to the east. Some of the smaller nodules with a patchy pink colour have a crust of dolomite or silica crystals. At intervals can be larger, more massive lenses usually referred to as alabaster and capable of being carved into tomb effigies as seen in Dunster Church and dating from the 15th and 16th centuries. The gypsum horizons can be picked out from the beach and are capped by a further 10m of predominantly grey and black shales and siltstones which top what is now called the Blue Anchor Formation. Formerly, these same beds might have been termed "Rhaetic". That unit was always identified in the mind of geologists with a 'Rhaetic Bone-Bed', a lag accumulation, caused by a winnowing out of bony material by currents, of fish scales, teeth and coprolite pellets together with crystalline iron pyrites, the last resulting from the foul-bottom sulphidic muds. Like the familiar Ludlow Bone-Bed of the Welsh Borderlands, the bone-bed acquired a certain time significance which it hardly deserved. In the Somerset coast sequences there are many bone-beds throughout the 30-40m of the Blue Anchor Formation, not all continuous.

The cliff here is dangerous to climb, but sufficient blocks have dropped to the beach to give a good idea of the bone-bed lithology, identifiable by the rusty weathering of the iron pyrites. This must be the main bonus from collecting at Blue Anchor. Bedding surfaces in split blocks can be covered by the well-formed shapes of bivalve molluscs of a kind called 'modiola' or 'mytiliform' suggestive of well established tidal flat or shallow shore facies in the higher dark beds. However, single specimens can be found right through the sequence, hinting at a transition from freshwater marl conditions to marine nearshore. This is confirmed by the incoming of trace fossils such as *Arenicolites* and *Diplocraterion* usually associated with intertidal situations.

Probably these gradual changes are best followed by walking at low water across the rock ledges of St Audrie's Bay, examining the top surfaces. Similar successions also occur between Splash Point, Watchet and Helwell Bay grading upwards into the lowest Lias, and seen from the beach at Watchet West Beach though much disturbed by faulting and landslipping. What is mainly missing compared with the famous sections of Aust and Garden Cliffs further north on the banks of the Severn are accessible outcrops of the Cotham Marble and White Lias which, although they do occur at the very top of the Blue Anchor cliff, are well out of reach. They are represented in some of the fallen blocks.

WATCHET FORESHORE

Having visited the Triassic-Jurassic transition beds in the critical cliff section at Blue Anchor it is now worthwhile exploring the sections occurring on either side of Watchet Harbour. To the west (towards Blue Anchor) the beds are highly disturbed by folding, most of which is a consequence of closely-spaced lateral slip stresses so that packets of strata ranging from the Penarth Group (formerly Rhaetic) to Lower Lias are buckled into sharp crested folds and slid into close juxtaposition. Not an easy location to piece together a true stratigraphical succession. East of the harbour, from below the East Pier and stretching from Splash Point (the cliff capped by the white relay mast) and the west side of Doniford Bay, the transition from the Westbury Formation (Penarth Group) is little disturbed in a sequence of hard and soft bands extending seawards. Standing on the cliff below Splash Point (ST 077436) it is possible at low water to pick out minor faults offsetting the strata, lines sometimes exploited by the sea, but effectively the succession here is free of major faulting or folding.

The cliff itself and the bluff behind the boat repair shed on the quay exposes red Mercia Marls dipping seawards at about 20 degrees, followed across the immediate foreshore by about 20m of Blue Anchor Formation siltstones and shales, including horizons which may correlate with the gypsum-bearing levels of Blue Anchor Cliff. However, gypsum nodules and veins are not evident though disturbances in the marls may reflect subsequent leaching of the salt. Further out, towards low water mark, a sequence some 15m thick representing the Westbury Formation comprises sandy limestone bands, shales with pyrites, bone-beds and shales with fibrous gypsum ('beef'). Bivalve shells and trace fossils signify near-shore marine conditions indicating transition towards the full marine transgression of the lowermost Jurassic. That attainment is marked by very distinctive tough shale/mudstone sheets which carry the iridescent ammonite *Psiloceras planorbis*, the lowest of the accepted ammonite zones of the Jurassic System.

In following this succession away from the foot of the pier and the cliff care must be taken at all times to note the state of the tide and avoid getting cut off as channels and fault zones fill early on the returning tide on the shoreward side.

Access to the east shore can be from the East Pier (ST 074437) through a gate in the fence, and by steps (caution: seaweed) with a gap to the nearest sandstone. Alternatively, from the dip in the cliff top path to Helwell Bay (ST 075436) or from

Helwell Bay having descended the concrete steps from the car park field (ST 078435). Car parking is possible at the end of the lane leading to the football ground from the Doniford Road heading for the Doniford Caravan Camp (private). Cross the railway and free parking is to the left of the track.

WATCHET WEST BEACH

As explained earlier this is not a locality where the stratigraphy can be worked out easily because of the faulting on the foreshore. Nevertheless, a walk along this shore gives a chance to decipher some of the fault pattern and also appreciate the nature of the gypsum/alabaster occurrence first seen at Blue Anchor.

Access is from a slipway dropping steeply from West Street at a gap in the continuous terrace of houses (Fig.4). From that slipway note the dip of the red marls and siltstones in the cliff immediately in front and the buckling down dip. This was a point of weakness in the sea defences of the town, a situation countered by coastal defence engineering and of some interest. The slipway is incorporated into a high concrete wall curving at the top to refract waves. Storms are capable of throwing beach pebbles over the houses on to the road beyond. Some of that force is now dissipated by massive blocks of dolerite or diorite, of unknown provenance, scattered at the foot of the slope. Some of the igneous blocks are rich in feldspars others are a denser more uniform greenstone. Exotic stone of a different type occurs in the wall which backs the small sandy bay. A dense black limestone is patterned by twig-like clusters of the coral *Lithostrotion*, proving that it is a Carboniferous Limestone. The coral is accompanied by thin-shelled *Productus* valves suggesting an early Viséan age. These are fossils which should not be collected. The armour stone was supplied by Foster Yeoman from Tor Quarry, Frome in their own freight trains via the West Somerset Railway.

It is worthwhile looking at the pebbles and boulders which are thrown up in this sandy bay and elsewhere, such as the paddling pool. Waves and tides bring them in from the offshore ledges and reefs and can be the best way of acquiring specimens of Jurassic fossils without struggling across the broken outcrops and their intervening water-filled channels. Blue-grey limestones crowded with bivalves in cross-section, slabs with bedding surfaces covered with monospecific modioliforms and the occasional *Pecten* are the rule. Some limestones show ribbon-form traces of bivalve burrowing which, with U-shaped burrows, give some idea of the Liassic shore ecology.

To get on to the main beach it is necessary to pick your way along the strike outcrops of red sandstone which curve away from the paddling pool. These beds belong to the Blue Anchor Formation some distance above the red Mercia Marls, which outcrop in the high cliff behind the small beach. Note that the dips on the foreshore are generally seawards, while the dip in the cliff is landwards. The line of the fault separating the two must run behind the concrete steps, which climb and descend a sandstone bluff. This is not a good access route as the other side lands you into a loose scree of rounded limestone boulders which are difficult underfoot.

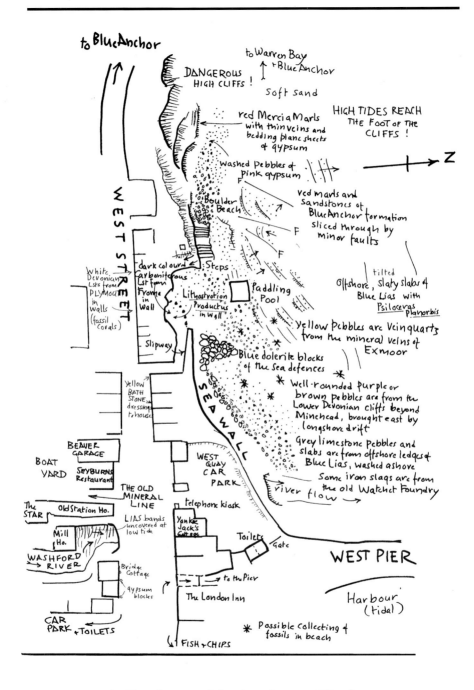

Figure 4. Sketch map of the foreshore at Watchet.

Verging to the right below the bluff is both safer and more instructive. Looking at the sandstone ridges you become aware that the jointing becomes close-spaced, suggesting proximity to fault lines. The outcrops are indeed whale-shaped and tapered by such faults. The deformation involved has produced slickensided surfaces and there is evidence of small scale thrusts. The patterns are those which result when normal outcrops are squeezed by strike-slip faults - a hint of the larger scale regional stresses.

Looking out to sea some upturned beds can catch the eye. These are the tough mudstones (lowermost Lias) of almost a slaty character which carry the recognisable discs of *Psiloceras planorbis*, preserved either as white outlines or shell having an iridescent mother-of-pearl lustre. These beds are repeated by faulting towards Warren Bay.

At this point along the beach attention is drawn to a low red marl cliff laced with thin string veins of gypsum occasionally swelling to become a white nodule. The veins follow the bedding and joints, slipping from one level to another. The latter suggests mobility of the mineral-rich brines synchronous with or post-dating the joints and faults. Was this a late Mesozoic event ? Or did it occur during Tertiary times? The question remains open (Firman, 1989).

Moving further westwards the cliffs rise and some of the horizons in the marl develop much larger masses of gypsum. These are the ones which historically were taken to Watchet Harbour, loaded on ships for Bristol and converted into plaster-of-paris to meet the Victorian hunger for busts and plaques for mantlepieces and piano tops. Nowadays it would be to make plaster boards, but gathering is no longer undertaken other than to provide small carvings or geological specimens for visitors.

As the cliffs grow higher, by standing back on the beach, it is possible to see in one perspective the three-dimensional structure formed by the cliff faces and the rocky outcrops of the foreshore. The cliffs exhibit sequences of red, grey-green and dark coloured layers appearing to rise and fall in pitched roof patterns, the darker (Lias) let down in trapdoor-like wedges. Some surfaces seen slightly obliquely are actual fault planes with slicken surfaces and they have tended to become slip surfaces of subsequent landslips. When the bouldery beach is swept clean by storms the wedges and fault lines can be traced onto the foreshore. All is summarised by the Geological Survey in the Minehead Memoir (Edwards, 2000, fig. 35), especially in the work on inverted extensional fault systems in the Bristol Channel coastal areas (Dart *et al* 1995).

Warning must be given of the instability of these cliffs. Falls are happening all the time as evidenced by the large tilted masses on the beach. The wearing of a hard hat is advisable. This stretch of cliffs is unprotected by an armour of stone blocks which might safeguard the caravan sites on the Blue Anchor road, which has a shifting foundation. The expense is too great.

WATCHET TOWNSCAPE

If scrambling over stony beaches or tackling the steep slopes of the Quantocks becomes too stressful then why not fall back on the geology of the streets and harbour? Several of the cottages around the harbour with a medieval street plan can be as old as the 16th century. Although many are rendered, some stand as Somerset vernac-

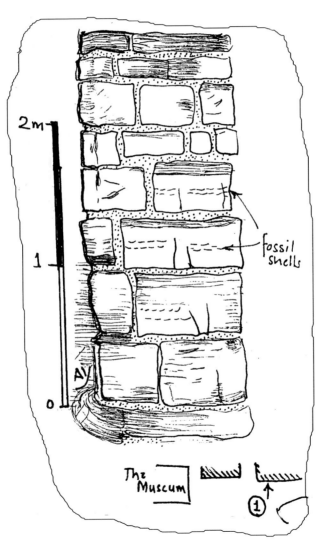

Figure 5 (a) Gatepost to The Headlands.

ular and their rubble walling, if visible, will be of Lias slabs, squared blocks of the thicker Lias limestone bands intermixed with some Palaeozoic Exmoor slates and rounded beach boulders, some exotic brought in as ship's ballast in the 19th century. As such 'wall games' abound and have been drafted on A4 sheets for short stay visitors to the town, whose appetite for stones has been whetted at the Town Museum in Swain Street. Walls, such as those found surrounding the three main car parks and lining lanes leading up to the more modern estates, are the subject of a booklet which can be bought at outlets on the streets (*A Geology of Watchet Walls*, Robinson, 2005).

As an example close to the museum entrance, at the top of the main slipway to the modern Marina, the gatepost to *The Headlands* (Fig. 5a) offers a substantial wall of blocks of Lias limestones, most neatly trimmed and squared. A number of different lithologies are represented. There is a dense blue-grey mudstone (a fine grained impure limestone), the chosen material for lime-burning and the production of hydraulic lime, no additives needed, for which Watchet was famous. Used in sea-

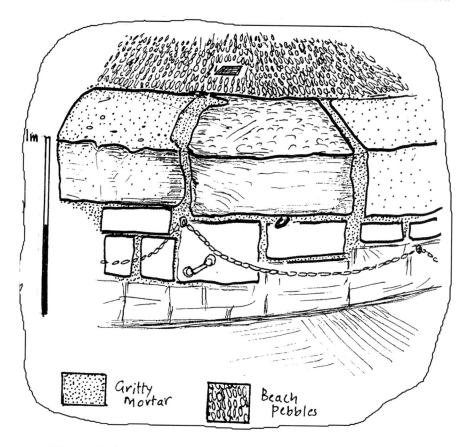

Figure 5 (b) Harbour wall at the top of the slipway.

walls and harbours, it received special mention when Smeaton was building his lighthouses in the late 18th and early 19th centuries. Note the projecting outlines of bivalves on the smooth surfaces of the blocks which pick out the original floor of the Jurassic sea bed. One or two of the blocks retain a friable flaky top, usually scalped off, which weathers badly. Calcite veining and cavities occur in others caused by contraction of the soft muds during lithification, the secondary calcite infillings showing a crystalline spar-like habit in the cavities.

On the opposite side of the slipway the wall to the Esplanade and the Harbour Wall is topped by massive blocks of stone, several tonnes in weight (Figure 5b). Some are grey, others a dull red colour. Look at the grey ones and note that the top surface carries raised bumps, regular in shape and outline. These are the moulds of bivalve fossils, some retaining their silvery shell at the margins. One or two have the platy laminated shell of oysters. These traces of fossils prove that there is a more substantial limestone band within the local Lias succession. The dull red rocks are gritty sandstones with visible sand grains and occasional pebbles of quartz. It is thought that these sandstones were quarried from one of the Williton quarries working Triassic sandstones overlying the pebble beds (see p. 8). These quarries supplied harbour and pier building materials for all the ports of the Bristol Channel coast and were an important export for the port of Watchet.

The decorative mosaic underfoot of the Esplanade walk is formed of elliptical pebbles of Lower Devonian Hangman Grit, the stone of the cliffs at Minehead, reduced in transit alongshore to Watchet. Pebble mosaic is a long-established habit for paving in Watchet, sometimes in decorative patterns when colours are selected carefully.

A short distance along the Esplanade stands a statue of Coleridge's *Ancient Mariner* by the Scottish sculptor Alan Herriot, erected in 2001. Watchet claims this association in the belief that the poet may have encountered a seaman who inspired the story and then completed the long narrative poem in the ancient ale house, *The Bell*, in company with his friend William Wordsworth. Geological interest in the commanding monument lies in the substantial stone pedestal supporting the bronze. This is in Capton Stone, a very well-cemented red sandstone, almost quartzitic and flecked with calcite veins, within the Lower Sandstone (= Otter Sandstone of the Geological Survey) of the local Triassic. Capton is a small hamlet just beyond Samford Brett and has the only working quarry to survive in West Somerset (see p.8).

Track back to Swain Street and find No. 32 which shows striking irregular shaped pieces of white stone bound within a fierce example of ribbon pointing (Fig.5c). The stone deserves close inspection for it reveals fossils which prove it is Middle Devonian reefal limestone of the kind amply found in and around Plymouth. The tell-tale fossils are favositid tabulate corals and rugose corals, such as *Acanthophyllum* and the colonial *Phillipsastrea,* accompanied by crinoid ossicles. Watchet boats were regular visitors to Plymouth and the South Devon Coast in the late 19th century and the limestone must have been used as ship's ballast. Further examples can be seen in a whole terrace of houses (1880) extending up West Street on the Blue Anchor Road, on the harbour road alongside the

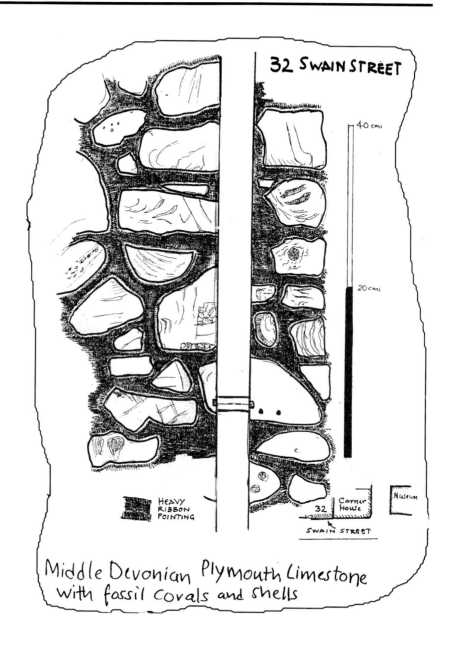

Figure 5. (c) No. 32 Swain Street.

Methodist Church and at Almyr House up Goviers Lane.

In the large car parks of Watchet the walls are constructed of much more varied materials. Liassic stones, recycled from demolished buildings include all the lithologies seen in the walls to *The Headlands*. If they have been collected from the beaches they may include blocks pitted by the drillings of a sponge such as *Cliona*. Some massive limestone blocks may be patterned by paler strips (actually tubes) left by burrowing bivalves active in the Lias seas. Purple and drab Lower Devonian sandstones from Minehead occur together with rusty-coloured vein quartz, probably from the Exmoor ore workings. More exotic material includes Carboniferous Pennant Sandstone from South Wales, Carboniferous Limestone from South Wales, Weston-super-Mare, Clevedon or the Bristol area and granites possibly of Cornish origin. The searcher will always be keen to discover stone from Lundy Island, which had a strong link with Watchet traffic, or the Scilly Isles. It is this which makes wall surveys interesting.

Watchet has suffered several destructive storms affecting the Bristol Channel the most celebrated as recently as 1900. In spite of this several 16th century cottages survive clustered on Swain Street and Main Street. Their proportions give a clue to their antiquity. Mid-Victorian houses and shops on Swain Street made a habit of including keystones to windows and doors of local alabaster. Weathering has usually etched these blocks to an extent which makes them resemble carvings. Plaster rendering obscures much else.

Finally, it is worthwhile visiting Watchet Railway Station and its Jubilee Geological Wall located midway along the very long platform. In 1857 Watchet was identified by Brunel as a port busy enough to warrant linkage to his Great Western network at Taunton. He duly surveyed the route as was his habit with a keen eye for gradients and curves best able to give a smooth ride for his 7ft wide broad gauge track. He also sized up the prospects for the supply of good quality stone for bridges, culverts and substantial station buildings, He identified Woolston Quarry, one or two quarries in Williton and Washford, all in red Triassic rocks, and the Blue Lias at Watchet. Watchet was the terminus when the line was finally completed in 1862, two years after Brunel's death. His mark remains in the width of the track bed, broad enough to accommodate two lines of the 4ft 8$^{1}/_{2}$in standard gauge, the red sandstone of the station buildings and the grey Lias cementstone blocks of the original goods shed, now the Boat Museum. The shed features a unique Watchet Flatner inshore fishing boat. Note the crusty weathering and resulting pillow shapes of the blocks. The cementstone forms the walls of the small Lamp Room on the right-hand side of the platform and just a little distance beyond, in the long embankment, occurs as a natural outcrop dipping at about 15 degrees towards the coast. There are four such bands of limestone separated by flaky yellow weathering shales or sticky grey clay. The fourth forms the base of the original Signalbox which controlled access to the harbour side. The box was demolished during the Beeching years of the 1960's and the line closed until 1976 when it was rescued and became the West Somerset Railway running for some 35km, the longest privately owned line in England. In 1999 the basal courses of the Lias slab-stones were made the foundation for what is now the Watchet Jubilee Geological Wall, bringing together all the minerals, fossils and rock types associated with the town and district.

The workforce for this enterprise came from the Seahorse Centre in Minehead, an activity centre for people with learning difficulties and other handicaps. Work in the community was their opportunity to express themselves, collecting from the beach and begging specimens from local gardens as a preliminary to building the wall under the supervision of staff and local people volunteering their practical skills. It took nearly two years to complete but, in the process, gained valuable local interest and that of rail passengers. The Seahorse effort won for them a LASMO award in 2002 and funding for a descriptive leaflet which can be bought (10p or a donation) at the Booking Office shop. Geological wall building of this type is recommended for other groups as a way of reaching out to the non-geological community.

Now walk the length of the platform to reach the level crosssing noticing the badly weathered rails on the right-hand side supporting the fencing. These are the original flat-bellied rails of the Brunel broad gauge track. When the line was extended to the growing seaside resort of Minehead in 1874 the line switched to the standard 4ft 8½in. gauge. The first road bridge crossing the line beyond the station has adequate clearance only for this width of line so care needs to be taken in leaning out of the train windows but, from then on to Bishop's Lydeard the present terminus, there are no such hazards. In the future the proposal is to link the terminus with Taunton main line station about 6km away.

HELWELL BAY

An excursion within easy reach of Watchet is to Helwell Bay and Doniford to the east of the harbour (Fig. 6). Here there is access to more transitional sequences from the Triassic Mercia Marl upwards into the Lower Lias. Like the strata in front of the East Pier at Watchet these rocks are less disturbed by faulting and do contain more obvious Liassic fauna. The other point of interest in the bay is the evidence of Pleistocene events touched on earlier (p.8).

Using Figure 6 either drive along Doniford Road, taking the minor road leading to the Memorial Ground used by the Football Club, go over the rail bridge and into the small car park (free of charge), then follow the railed path to the steep cliff steps (take care) to the beach at Helwell Bay or walk from the level crossing at Goviers Lane along the path behind the Marina Offices via steps to the cliff top capped by the white telephone relay station, then follow the cliff top path which descends steeply to the cliff steps and beach. Note the remarkable flat surface which extends landwards and eastwards. Also from the pathway there are good views of Helwell Bay and the coast beyond, including St Audrie's and Kilve. At low water the bay below shows Lias limestone bands curving in sweeping lines across the foreshore suggestive of folding. Minor faults cause visible breaks in their continuity. Less easy to pick out are strike faults which cause ammonite zones to be cut out from the full standard succession. One such fault an east-west branch of the northwest-trending Watchet Fault, a major structure, causes significant disturbance

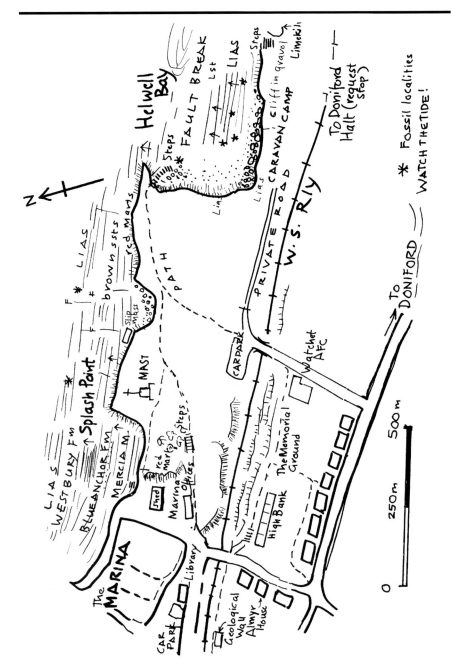

Figure 6. Sketch route map and geology of Helwell Bay area.

at the foot of the steps, although the actual fault-line is usually hidden by beach boulders and pebbles. To the left (north) forming the point and adjacent high cliffs is the Mercia Marl succession of red shales, harder grey-green siltstones and sandstones dipping seawards at between 20° and 30°. To the right (south), at the foot of the steps, are Liassic blue clays with *Gryphaea* ('Devil's Toenails') and loose blocks of limestone (Fig.6,). Nearby, can be found hard yellowish boulders and pebbles of quartz from mineral veins on Exmoor and hard purple Devonian sandstones from Minehead, moved eastwards along the coast by tidal action.

The top of the cliff hereabouts has a capping of even-sized pebbles generally orientated in an imbricate (overlapping) pattern. These are the Doniford Gravels which include lenses of sand, unfortunately not yielding organic remains suitable for dating purposes. The deposits occupy shallow channels which hint that the sequence is alluvial rather than coastal beach. The dramatically extensive flat surface mentioned above is equally clearly indicative of a marine planation at about 10-15m above present high water mark. Sea-level changes must have been a frequent event throughout the 2 million years of the Pleistocene whether the area was penetrated by glacial ice or not, with many options to talk of Anglian to Devensian timings. Only a correlation with the Bridgewater area and the peaty lowlands of the Parrett Valley, where the marine and brackish water Pleistocene Burtle Beds occur, will help to date the Doniford Gravels.

Moving towards the back of the bay note the large blocks of Palaeozoic greywacke-like sandstones , possibly from Triscombe Quarry in the Quantock Hills (p.5), and dark coloured Carboniferous Limestone being used for coastal protection. Helwell Bay is not backed by the customery Lias or Trias cliffs, but low clay and pebble bluffs which need protection from erosion. Capped by pockets of the Doniford Gravels what can be seen are the result of flows of mud and of pebbles which came off the Quantocks and Brendon Hills slopes during the periglacial climatic regimes of the Pleistocene. There must have been considerable volumes of meltwater during interglacial periods, sufficient to greatly enlarge the valleys now occupied by misfit streams, such as the Doniford Stream. This branch of the stream extends for some 1½ km to higher ground occupied by the Doniford Holiday Camp. Another branch of the same stream system can be followed swinging left through Williton and Danesfield to join the equally misfit Washford River flowing into the sea at Watchet. Both branches are characterised by marked gorges inland cutting through Trias/Lias sequences and caused by substantial meltwater flow.

The Liassic strata in the bay deserve close attention. They reveal fossil debris in pockets at the top of individual units, including small ammonites. Trace fossils also occur on the top surfaces and penetrating some limestone beds. Within about 100m of the west-east cliff line one of the tilted ledges carries on its top surface very large ammonites of the coroniceratid type, strongly ribbed and reaching a diameter of a minicar wheel. Do not try to remove these; leave for others to see; they break easily. The shells often carry an epifauna of oyster valves cemented in clusters on prominent high points. Clearly these oysters colonised a firm and upstanding 'island' upon the soft mud sea bed, that 'island' being a large dead ammonite come to rest with the benthos from its planktonic habitat. In a time sense these faunas represent the Sinemurian Stage and either the Kilve Shales or the Quantock Beds of the current classifications of Palmer (1972) or Whitaker (1983).

Midway along Doniford beach two distinct sectors of the foreshore quickly define themselves, an inner and outer set of prominent ledges of Lias limestones spaced apart by shale or mudstone interbeds. The ledges of the inner sector are more regular but cut by gaps which suggest small displacement faults, whereas the outer tend to curve and undulate as a result of lateral stresses buckling the outcrops. Between the two sectors is a broad mud-occupied gullet, running west-east across the bay and which is a hazard especially during rising tides. The gullet marks a continuance of the east-west branch line of the Watchet Fault, a strike fault, last seen at the steps. Fractures such as this are often re-activated by later earth movements and develop a strike-slip character. Indeed, it is even possible that the faults are located along older lines of faulting in the sub-structure created during the Hercynian earth movements, then revived during late Jurassic/pre-Greensand and mid-Tertiary movements. Also, the possibilities of adjustments during Pleistocene sea-level changes should not be ruled out. The shales of the outer sector Hettangian succession (the Aldergrove Beds) yield the distinctive ammonite *Psiloceras planorbis*, already mentioned at Watchet West Beach, and recognised as indicating the lowest of the Jurassic ammonite zones.

Midway along the beach, iron steps climb the clay and pebble cliff to reach a small car park (maximum 6 cars) and this is another good viewpoint (ST 087431). This location is convenient for access to the bay avoiding the walk along the cliff top from Watchet. For good measure it is the site of an interpretative board prepared by Taunton Museum. The car park is confined by a massive structure of dressed stone which has all the appearance of a military fortification. In fact, it is one of the more substantial of the surviving limekilns of the coast. Limestone blocks from the shore below were fed into the top of the kiln along with brushwood and cheap coal shipped directly from South Wales (Barry or Newport). The sailing vessels discharged on to the beach at high water. Lime burning either for soil improvement or for export as lime mortar was an active trade in the 18th-19th centuries, right up to the time when larger producers, such as the cementworks at Aberthaw on the opposite Glamorgan coast, became too competetive.

Similar kilns are close to the shore at Kilve and Lilstock. At St Audrie's Bay the remains of a large kiln survive rather serious erosion of the cliff. Today, there is an urgent need to conserve for historical reasons these surviving kiln units.

THE MINERAL LINE

The Mineral Line delivered iron-ore from the Brendon Hills mines to Watchet port between 1856 and the First World War. In its heyday it was a vital contributor to the employment and prosperity of the town. The mines and railway predate Brunel's line originally connecting with Taunton in 1862 (Sellick, 2003). If Heritage Funding is forthcoming a measure of restoration of the line and associated buildings can take place, increasing its tourist attraction.

From the West Quay, lines survive beneath the concrete of the West Quay car park and cross the road into the boatyard of the Watchet Boat Owners. Directly opposite a tall wedge-shaped building was the original station for the line, often carrying passengers up the Washford Valley to Comberow, 13km away. A tablet on the wall identifies it as 'Station House' with the date of 1857. Now a converted house, a long extension 'shed', once later a skittles alley, picks out the line of the original platform. Beyond the later building, Seyburns Restaurant, a much more substantial building was the engine shed. Built of red Triassic Lower Sandstone with dressings of grey Liassic limestone it is now Beaver's Garage.

Looking up the boatyard the line passes into a deep cutting flanked by out-crops of flaky grey Lias shales with thin limestone bands behind a screen of brambles. At the top of the yard the cutting has been infilled and houses in Whitehall built on the line track. From this point slip along Mill Lane, past The Star, and into Whitehall, following finger posts indicating 'Mineral Line'. At the top of Whitehall a lane breaks off to the right and passes beneath the younger West Somerset Line to Minehead. From then on, for almost 5km, a very pleasant green path follows the track exactly to Washford. Any roughness underfoot is caused by the original ballast for the track (Figure 7).

Nearly opposite to the hill capped by St Decuman's Church (St Decuman being a patron of Watchet in the 6th century but unfortunately died by decapitation) the valley narrows, a consequence of having been cut by periglacial meltwaters. The valley is virtually filled by the massive paper recycling Wansborough Mill, one of the largest in Western Europe. It is fed by millions of gallons of water taken from the Washford River but returned 'scrubbed clean'. Beyond the mill the valley opens up and the line runs through broad water meadows as far as Kentsford Farm. At the level crossing there is the opportunity to return to Watchet either by climbing the hill to the right and taking the Blue Anchor Road or crossing to the farm and taking a field path climbing to the church and its Holy Well. The route through the farm-yard gives the opportunity to appreciate that what is now a barn is really a long house (cattle and residents in the same building), one of several set up by the Cistercians of Cleeve Abbey, beyond Washford. Look at the details of the upper windows and the door posts of the main entrance for 13-14th century masoncraft. The present farmhouse is probably equally ancient but overprinted with Georgian facades.

Back on the line the path continues for a further 2½ km, passing another Abbey farm on the other side of the West Somerset Line, until it reaches the Recreation Ground of Washford village. Here, the path veers to the right but the track continues as a raised embankment to the village allotments. By following the winding lanes through the fringe of the village the busy A39 Williton-Minehead road is reached. By the telephone kiosk on the left-hand side of the road there is a gate leading down to domestic garages. This is private land but not totally out of bounds to genuinely interested visitors seeking the mineral line. The objective is to see a well-formed tunnel built of red sandstone which took the line beneath the coach road of the 1850's. The tunnel masonry is a testimony to the high standard of

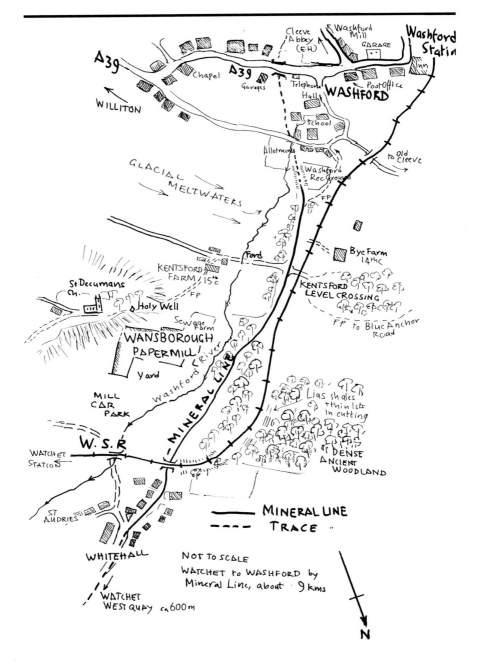

Figure 7. Sketch route map along part of the Mineral Line, Watchet to Washford.

work associated with this mid-19th century economic venture.

It is now possible, in season, to catch one of the hourly trains from Washford Station back to Watchet and Minehead. The station is also a small museum to the Somerset & Dorset Railway, which crossed the Mendips. Alternatively, it is worthwhile extending the walk a further 3km up the valley to Cleeve Abbey, an English Heritage site, and an important Cistercian power house for the wealth of this area after its foundation in 1188. The source of the increasing prosperity was wool and grain and it is interesting that an 'unconformity' can be detected in the walls reflecting this increase. The lower walls are of rounded cobbles or roughly dressed blocks of sandstone, both red in colour. They immediately suggest the local New Red Sandstone as a source, outcropping down the valley. Two centuries later, when more prosperous, warm coloured Dundry Stone from just south of Bristol was brought in by sea to Watchet. This Jurassic limestone invited the craftsmanship seen in the vaulting and tracery of the main building, on a par with what can be admired in St Mary Redcliffe and the Cathedral in Bristol. It gives an insight into Cistercian skills soon to be snuffed out in the Dissolution of the Monasteries.

Pressing on up the valley to Hungerford Farm and the White Horse pub, take a minor road fork to the left. This soon leads to the settlement called Torre. Here, there was a level crossing taking the mineral line across the road to a local cider farm (Torre) and the more distant village of Monksilver (worth visiting by car). Torre retains a small stone shed roofed with Treborough Slate (Devonian) from up the valley. This was a crossing-keeper's hut controlling traffic when the line was active. Look up the valley and the course of the track and a small embankment can be clearly seen. On the left-hand side of the crossing and road, a 5-8m high wall of natural sandstone outcrops. The beds are near vertical and were once a quarried face from which stone was taken for buildings and bridges up and down the line. It was one of the prime sources of building stone during the 1856-1860 construction period and can be seen again across the valley by the side of the road to Roadwater (TG 043402) alongside a lime kiln.

This is probably a convenient point to end this particular excursion from Watchet. Refreshment can be taken at the White Horse. The return journey can be by steam train from Washford Station.

TAILPIECES

"If this little work should succeed in awakening a greater interest in the beautiful scenery of this neighbourhood the author will feel that his work has not been in vain. It has been acknowledged by those persons who have had an opportunity of seeing the beauties of foreign lands, that a great deal of the West Somerset scenery has not been surpassed; we often wonder that parties should be so anxious to travel in other lands before they have seen half the beauties of their own" (quotation from Daniel Mackintosh, a geologist from Blairgowrie, in a local guide to Watchet *Geology of the Neighbourhood* 1867 by James Date, a noted photographer).

When Etheridge, a Scot and palaeontologist to the Geological Survey, " *first arrived on the ground, an active, vigorous and withal tender-hearted man, the contemplation of the great moorland hills and the folded, fractured and cleaved character of the rocks gave him such an impression of the immensity of his task, that he sat down and wept. He was not, however, a man to be daunted, and he set to work with persistent energy.*" (qotation from Woodward's *History of the Geological Society of London* 1907, p.230).

FURTHER READING

Cope, J.C.W. & Bassett, M.G. 1987. Sediment sources and Palaeozoic history of the Bristol Channel area. *Proceedings Geol. Assoc.,* **98,** 315-320.

Dawkins, W.B. 1864. On the Rhaetic Beds and the White Lias of western Somerset, and the description of a new fossil mammal in the Grey Marlstone beneath the Bone-Bed. *Quarterly J. Geological Society,* **20,** 396-412.

Edwards, R.A. 2000, *The Minehead District.* Memoir B.G.S. 128pp.

Edmonds, E.A. 1985. *Geology of the Country around Taunton and the Quantock Hills.* Memoir B.G.S., 92pp.

Etheridge, R.H. 1872. Notes on the Physical Structure of the Watchett area, and the relationship of the Secondary rocks of the Devonian series of West Somerset. *Proc. Cotteswold Nat. Field Club,* 6, 35-48.

King, A. 1997. *Fossil Ammonites from the Somerset Coast.* Somerset County Museum Services/ English Nature, 18pp.

Martin, E.C. 1909. The probable source of the limestone pebbles in the Bunter conglomerates of West Somerset. *Geol. Magazine,* **46,** 160-165.

Mayall, M.J. 1981. The Late Triassic Blue Anchor Formation and the initial Rhaetian marine transgression in South West Britain. *Geol. Magazine,* **118,** 377-384.

Palmer, C.P. 1972. The Lower Lias (Lower Jurassic) between Watchet and Lilstock in north Somerset. *Newsletters in Stratigraphy,* **2,** 1-30.

Robinson, E. 2003. Field Meeting, Winter on the Somerset Coast 14-16th February 2003. *Proceedings Geol. Assoc.,* **114,** 375-379.

Robinson, E. 2004. The West Somerset Mineral Line heritage project. *Geology Today,* **20,** 204-206.

Robinson, E. 2005. *A Geology of Watchet Walls.* Private publication, Watchet, 11pp.

Sellick, R.J. 2003. *The Old Mineral Line.* Exmoor Press. 64pp.

Webby, B.D. 1965. The stratigraphy and structure of the Devonian rocks in the Brendon Hills of West Somerset. *Proceedings Geol. Assoc.,* **76,** 39-60.

Webby, B.D. 1966. The stratigraphyand structure of the Devonian rocks in the Quantock Hills, West Somerset. *Proceedings Geol. Assoc.,* **77,** 321-343.

Whitaker, A, 1983. *Geology of the Country around Weston-super-Mare.* B.G.S Memoir.